VIOLIN
89VN

W9-CZL-797

# SOLOS & ETUDES 1

## Correlated with ALL FOR STRINGS, Book 1
## by Gerald E. Anderson and Robert S. Frost

### The Collection

**SOLOS & ETUDES, Book 1** is a collection of 25 solos and 29 etudes for the string class and is written in a unison format for violin, viola, cello, and string bass. This supplement features exercises designed to reinforce technical development and also provides material for musical growth and enrichment. A wide variety of styles and composers are represented including original solos and etudes by Robert S. Frost and Gerald E. Anderson.

**SOLOS & ETUDES, Book 1** is correlated with *All for Strings, Book 1*, pages 21-48, and can be used concurrently with Book 1, or as a review upon completion of any string method. The unison format provides all stringed instruments with each complete solo and etude allowing for suitability in both string class and individual study settings.

**SOLOS & ETUDES, Book 1** is published for the following instruments:
Violin   Viola   Cello   String Bass

Piano Accompaniment
All piano accompaniments are provided in the Conductor's Score. However, the accompaniments are also published in a separate book so that they are available to students for private study, recitals, and additional practice.

ISBN 0-8497-3321-9

*May 3rd*

## ETUDE 1

Frost

## ETUDE 2

Frost

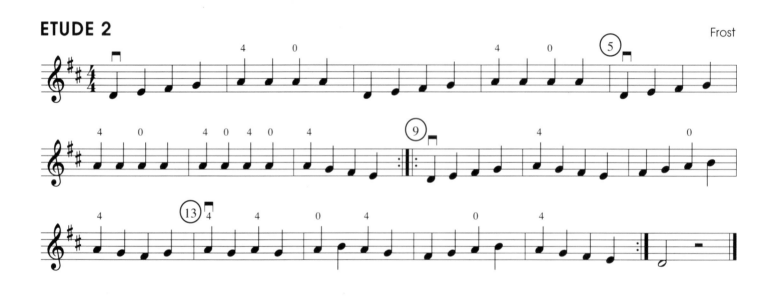

## ETUDE 3

Schradieck

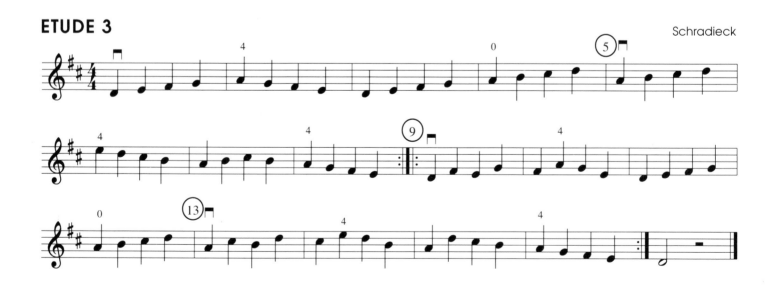

*ay 17th*

# RAMBLING

Anderson

*Del Segno al Fine*

# AUTUMN SUNRISE

Frost

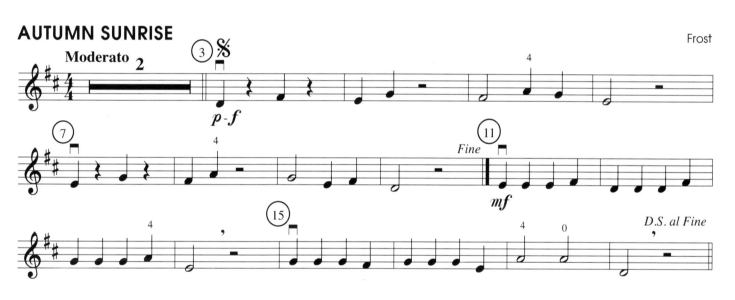

# RAINBOW RHUMBA

Anderson

4

## A JAZZ WALTZ

Anderson

mezzo forte

## FRENCH AIR

18th Century Tune

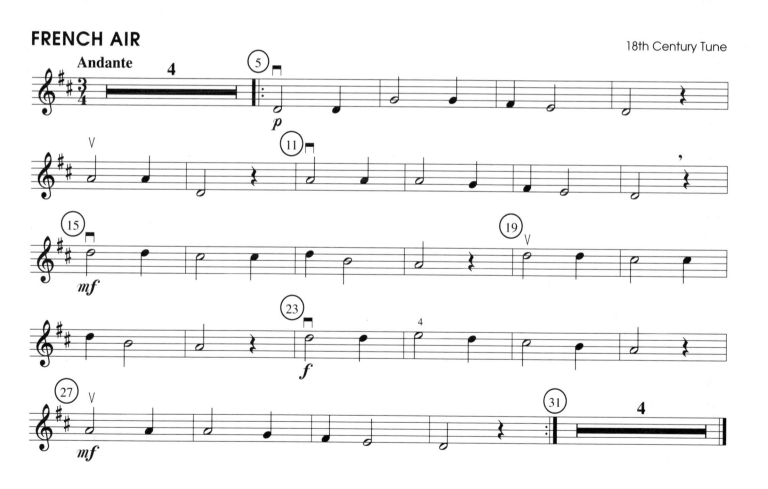

## ETUDE 8

Anderson

## ETUDE 9

Frost

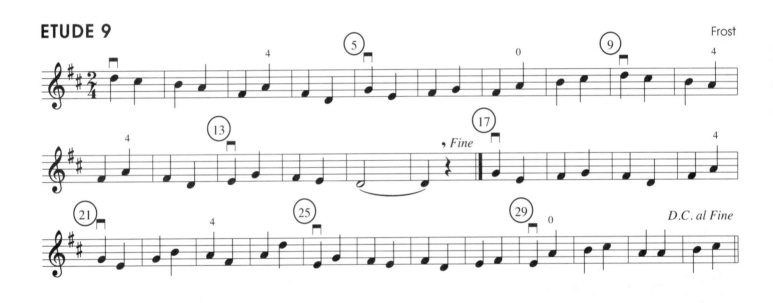

## ETUDE 10

Frost

## OUR SCHOOL MARCH

Anderson

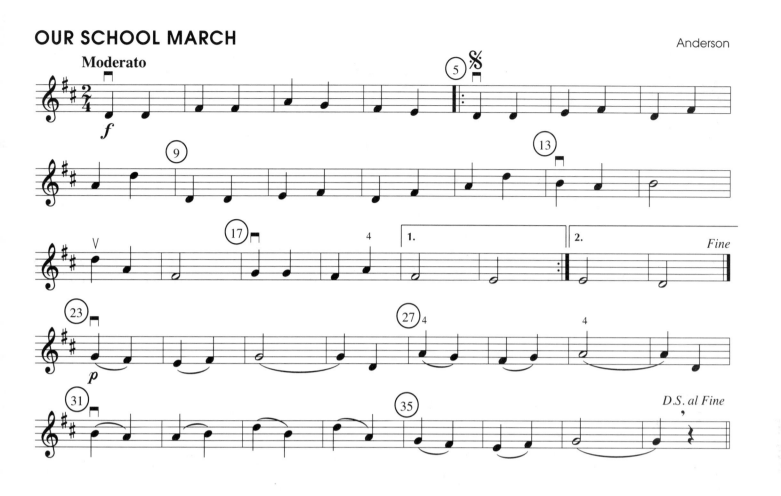

## SKIPPING ALONG

Anderson

## ETUDE 11

Frost

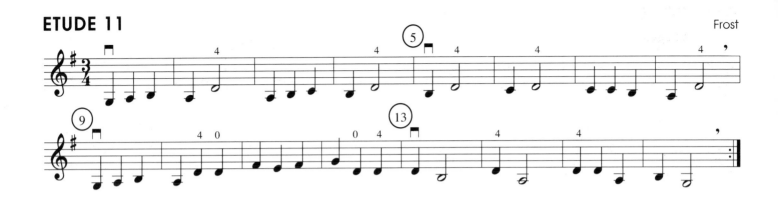

## ETUDE 12

Frost

## ETUDE 13

Frost

## GO PROUDLY

Brahms

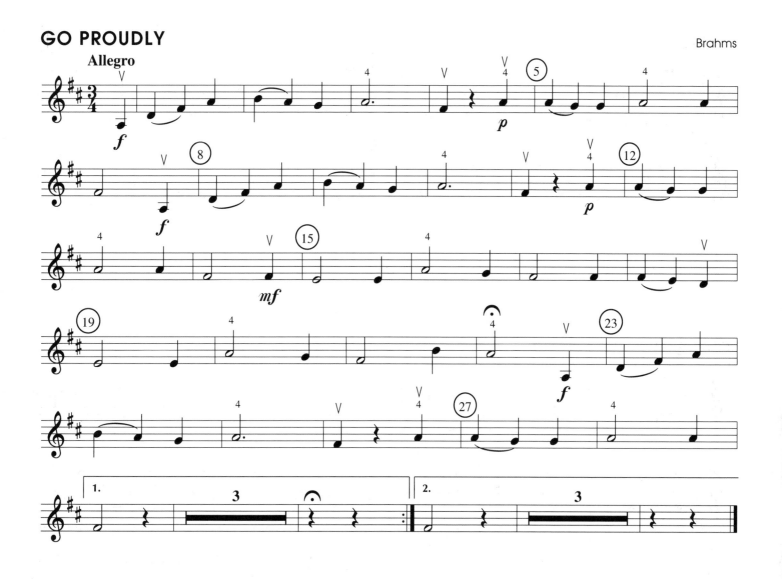

## SCARBOROUGH FAIR

English Folk Song

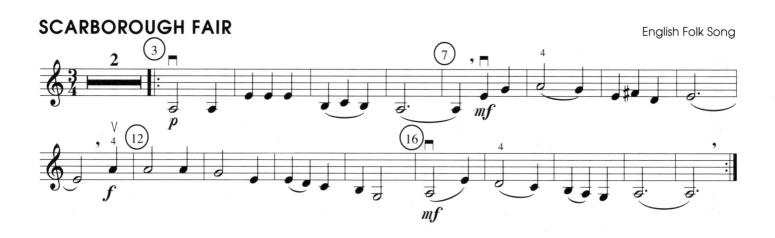

## ETUDE 14

Frost

## ETUDE 15

Frost

## ETUDE 16

Frost

## ETUDE 17

Frost

## GOLDEN MEDALLION
Frost

## GEE, ROCK!
Anderson

**ETUDE 18**

Frost

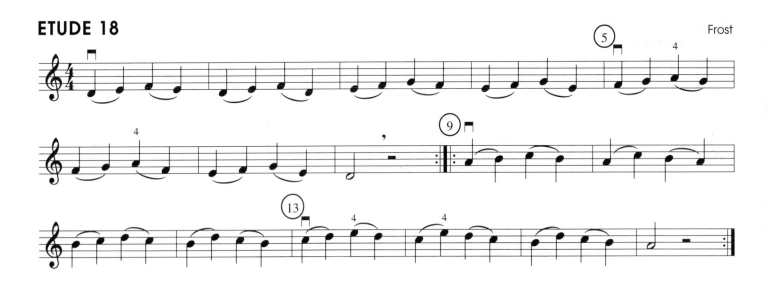

**ETUDE 19**

Wohlfahrt Op. 38, no. 39

**ETUDE 20**

Wohlfahrt Op. 45, no. 15

## POLLY OLIVER

Old English Air

## TSCHAIKOWSKY MEDLEY

Tschaikowsky

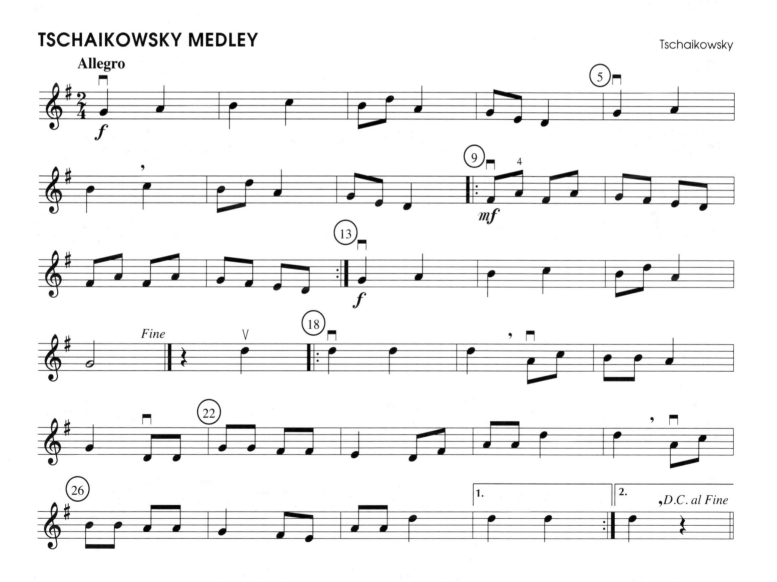

14

## ETUDE 21

Wohlfahrt Op. 38, no. 71

## ETUDE 22 DUET

Hermann Op. 20, no. 12

89VN

## TO FRIENDSHIP

Haydn

## MOCCASIN DANCE

Anderson

## ETUDE 23

Leonard - Carpentier

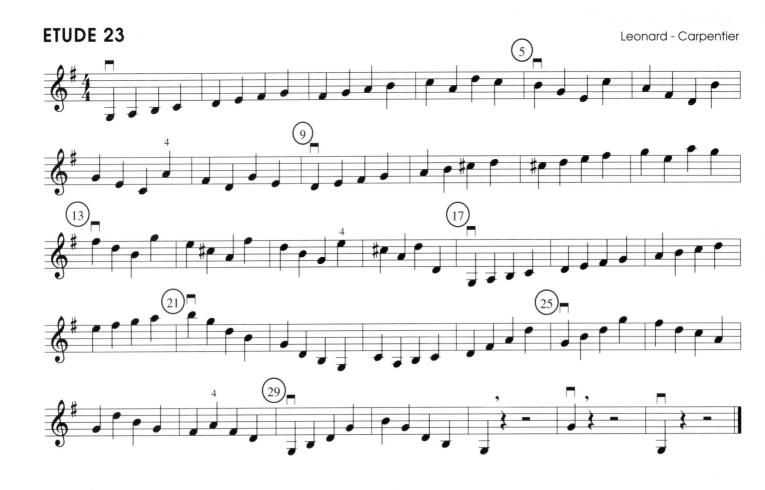

## ETUDE 24

Wohlfahrt Op. 38, no. 65

## GRANDMOTHER'S MINUET

Grieg Op. 68, no. 2

## POLKA

Wohlfahrt Op. 38, no. 38

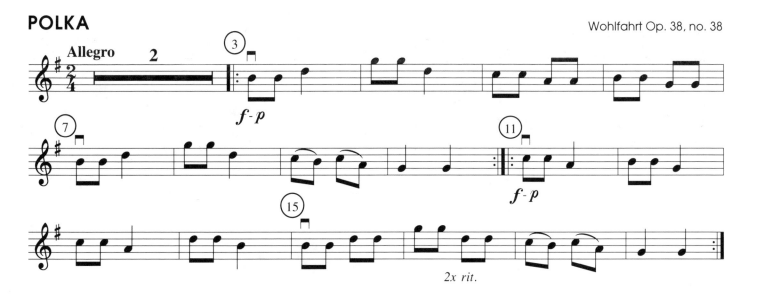

18

## ETUDE 25

Anderson

## ETUDE 26 DUET

Hohmann

89VN

# MINUET

Telemann

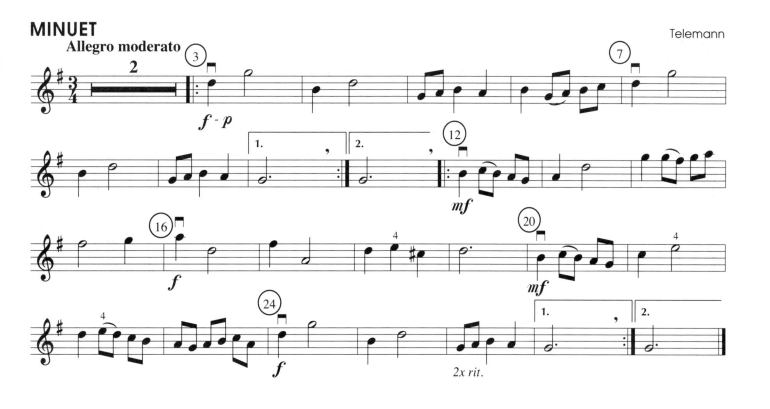

# SONATINA

Beethoven

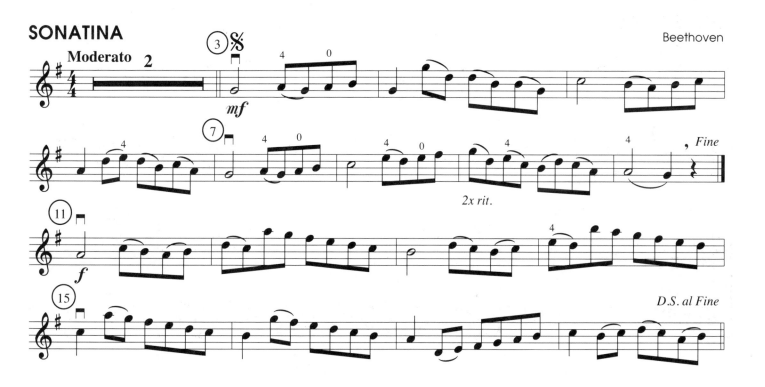

## ETUDE 27

Wohlfahrt Op. 38, no. 48

## ETUDE 28

Frost

## ETUDE 29

Anderson

## LITTLE ROSE BUD

Brahms

**Andante con moto**

## GOIN' SHOPPIN'

Frost

**Allegro**

*Play the repeat on the D.S.

# COME TO THE SEA

Venetian Melody

## THEME AND VARIATIONS

Papini Op. 57, no. 1

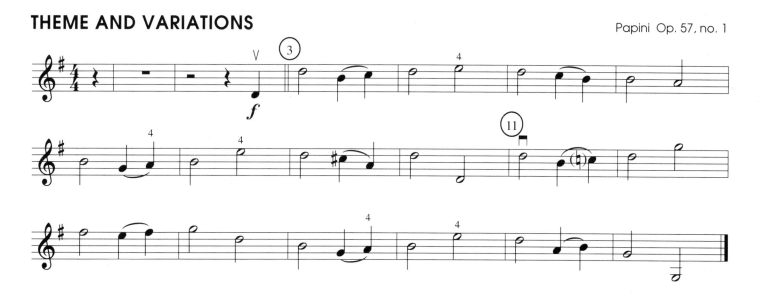

## 1st Variation

## 2nd Variation

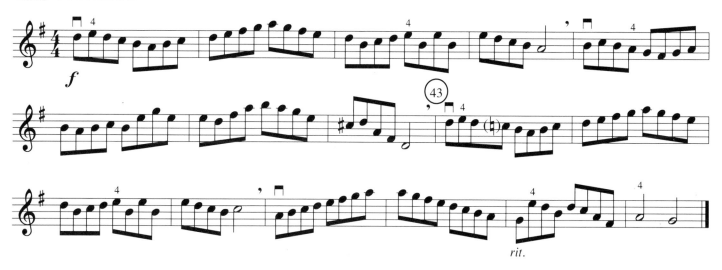

## GOOD NEIGHBORS ALL from the Peasant Cantata

J.S. Bach

## ROCKIN'

Anderson